WORD CHALLENGES
FOR SHARP MINDS

Larry J. Zembala

DALE SEYMOUR PUBLICATIONS

Illustrations: Rachel Gage

ISBN 0-86651-448-1
Order number DS03800

DALE
SEYMOUR
PUBLICATIONS
P.O. BOX 10888
PALO ALTO, CA 94303

5 6 7 8 9 10 11 12 13-MA-95 94 93

CONTENTS

INTRODUCTION

Word Challenges for Sharp Minds is intended to spice up your language arts curriculum. The puzzles found within this book will not only enhance language skills, but will challenge students to exercise their creative and critical thinking skills.

This book, originally published as *Grand Slam,* grew out of the author's work with a particular gifted student. Colleagues and parents soon became interested in the book, and it proved to be very popular in the author's home state of Indiana. This new edition includes expanded and improved activities.

How you use these activities in your classroom will vary depending on your teaching style and the ability of your students. The activities have been used successfully as individual, small-group, and large-group tasks. They are also effective as learning center activities and early morning eye-openers.

Each blackline master can be used independently. Answers are provided beginning on page 63.

EXPANDING WORDS

Read each set of clues below. After figuring out the first word,
add one letter to the beginning of it to form the second word.
The first one has been done as an example.

1. Add one letter to a playing card, and you have a fixed rate of running.

    _____ACE_____   _____PACE_____

2. Add one letter to what a movie star does, and you have a treaty.

    _____   _____

3. Add one letter to an insect, and you will be breathing very heavily.

    _____   _____

4. Add one letter to the U.S. national bird, and you have a dog.

    _____   _____

5. Add one letter to a sea creature, and you have part of a fishing pole.

    _____   _____

6. Add one letter to a word that means spoken, and you have something you find in the sea.

    _____   _____

7. Add one letter to a unit of length, and you have something you can do with your fingers.

    _____   _____

8. Add one letter to a word that means command, and you have the edge of something.

    _____   _____

9. Add one letter to a skin sensation, and you have a narrow trench.

    _____   _____

10. Add one letter to a word that means inquire, and you have another word for work.

    _____   _____

11. Add one letter to a word that indicates pain, and you have something you might sit on.

    _____   _____

VOWEL CHANGE

Read each set of clues below. After figuring out the first word, change only its vowels to form the second word. The first one has been done as an example.

1. Having much strength STRONG   A thin cord STRING

2. A gale _____   Magician's stick _____

3. To revolve _____   Ripped _____

4. To inform _____   A fee _____

5. Close loudly _____   Thin _____

6. To throw _____   Small piece of cloth _____

7. A deep dish _____   To cry loudly _____

8. To break slightly _____   A fellow _____

9. To wink _____   Something you fill in _____

10. Take a small drink _____   Tree juice _____

11. Sea mammal _____   Dirt _____

12. Unit of time _____   Possessive pronoun _____

13. Mild temperature _____   Legless burrower _____

14. Turn rapidly _____   Period of time _____

15. To clean _____   To want _____

16. A mist _____   A type of snake _____

17. A backless seat _____   A type of metal _____

18. To hurry _____   Skin irritation _____

19. To mix _____   Without sight _____

20. Shout of approval _____   Piece of furniture _____

21. Center _____   To confuse _____

METAMORPHOSIS I

Read each set of clues below. After figuring out the first word, change only one of its letters to make the second word. The first one has been done as an example.

1. A playing card __ACE__   A verb of being __ARE__

2. A measure of land _____   A dull pain _____

3. A fight _____   A container for soda _____

4. A flat piece of wood _____   Facial hair _____

5. A strong rope _____   Where dinner is eaten _____

6. Enclosure for animals _____   Leaf of a book _____

7. A vehicle _____   A prank _____

8. Business agreement _____   To get better _____

9. Part of your body _____   To consume _____

10. To pass out _____   An artist's medium _____

11. A large meal _____   A wild animal _____

12. A stinging insect _____   To breathe with difficulty _____

13. An outdoor sport _____   A dog's relative _____

14. A dwelling place _____   A racing animal _____

15. Sound of a bell _____   A tropical forest _____

METAMORPHOSIS II

Read each set of clues below. After figuring out the first word, change only one of its letters to make the second word. The first one has been done as an example.

1. Found in a courtroom JUDGE   A sweet substance FUDGE

2. Part of a door _____   A stuck-up person _____

3. Tool for eating _____   To labor _____

4. Knot on your head _____   To walk with difficulty _____

5. Part of a tree _____   Unable to hear _____

6. A shopping area _____   Men and boys _____

7. Filled with fun _____   Compassion _____

8. Part of your body _____   A written message _____

9. Peculiar _____   Out of date _____

10. A tropical bird _____   A vegetable _____

11. A place to play _____   Meat from a pig _____

12. Very fast _____   A duck's sound _____

13. Type of bed cover _____   Pen made from a feather _____

14. Lots of noise _____   A spaceship _____

15. Precipitation _____   To destroy _____

METAMORPHOSIS III

Read each set of clues below. After figuring out the first word, change only one of its letters to make the second word. The first one has been done as an example.

1. Found at a beach __SAND__   Uttered __SAID__

2. Weighing device _____   To frighten _____

3. An action in football _____   Stroke with a feather _____

4. Simple _____   A direction _____

5. Very delicate _____   Part of a car _____

6. A baseball judge _____   A group of countries _____

7. To speak _____   A water mammal _____

8. A type of vehicle _____   To darken the skin _____

9. To bend out of shape _____   A type of fish _____

10. To use unwisely _____   Tongue's job _____

11. Sign of sleepiness _____   A young deer _____

12. To twist around _____   To locate _____

13. To sway back and forth _____   Turkey talk _____

14. Fur animal _____   Source of ore _____

15. An animal park _____   Also _____

"O" NO

Add two or more O's to each set of letters to form a word. The first one has been done as an example.

1. M T R   <u>MOTOR</u>

2. C L R   _____

3. M N S N   _____

4. P H T   _____

5. M T T   _____

6. V D   _____

7. F R G T   _____

8. F L L W   _____

9. B R N C   _____

10. S C H L   _____

11. F T S T L   _____

12. F L P R F   _____

13. S R R W   _____

14. T M R R W   _____

15. C L N   _____

16. S L   _____

17. H B   _____

18. R B T   _____

19. C C N   _____

20. C L N Y   _____

21. C M M N   _____

22. C N V Y   _____

23. D R   _____

Star of
a play

actor

"ACT" IT OUT

Each clue below suggests a word that contains the consecutive letters A-C-T. See how many you can do. Act now!

1. A building for making goods _____

2. A true statement _____

3. Closely packed together _____

4. To take out _____

5. To work at to get better _____

6. Very useful _____

7. To get in touch with _____

8. A farm machine _____

9. Precisely _____

10. To take away _____

11. A desert plant _____

12. Part of a whole _____

13. Measures angles _____

14. Microscopic organisms _____

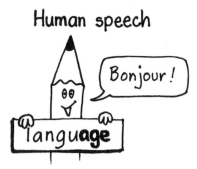
Human speech

Bonjour!

language

WHAT IS YOUR "AGE"?

Each clue below suggests a word that ends with the letters
A-G-E. See how many you can do, whatever your age.

1.   A vegetable   _____

2.   A lack of something   _____

3.   What travelers take   _____

4.   Ocean trip   _____

5.   Place to park the car _____

6.   Valor   _____

7.   To harm   _____

8.   Fierce   _____

9.   Type of breakfast meat _____

10. Mailing fee   _____

11. A pet bird's home   _____

12. A communication   _____

13. Fury   _____

14. A horse-drawn cart   _____

15. An actor's platform   _____

16. A small town   _____

To set in the
ground to grow **BET YOU C-"AN'T"**

Each clue below suggests a word that contains the consecutive letters A-N-T. See how many you can do. Bet you can't get them all!

1. Very large _____

2. A pachyderm _____

3. A national song _____

4. Imaginative fiction _____

5. Having great meaning or value _____

6. To breathe heavily _____

7. Empty _____

8. Word opposite in meaning _____

9. A place to eat _____

10. An amount _____

11. Sweet smelling _____

12. Far away _____

13. Part of the earth's interior _____

14. Agreeable or delightful _____

"ARE" YOU READY?

Each clue below suggests a word that contains the consecutive letters A-R-E. See how many you can do. Are you ready for these?

1. To look at angrily   _____

2. A four-sided figure   _____

3. Payment for travel   _____

4. To frighten   _____

5. Extra   _____

6. A word of warning   _____

7. Your mom or dad   _____

8. A type of trap   _____

9. A certain section or region   _____

10. A place for sports contests   _____

11. A signaling light   _____

12. Knowledgeable   _____

13. A female horse   _____

14. To divide and distribute   _____

I "ATE" THE WHOLE THING

Each clue below suggests a word that ends with the letters
A-T-E. See if you can do the whole thing.

1.   To act like someone else   _____

2.   To supply with water   _____

3.   To make angry   _____

4.   To turn into vapor   _____

5.   To complete high school   _____

6.   To find   _____

7.   A favorite flavor   _____

8.   You do this on ice   _____

9.   To ornament or adorn   _____

10. To pause briefly   _____

11. To split apart   _____

12. To make or invent   _____

13. Having a backbone   _____

14. Free from error   _____

15. Mathematical guess   _____

16. To teach or train   _____

17. A large wooden box   _____

18. To turn in a circle   _____

19. To honor with a ceremony   _____

20. To perform surgery   _____

A conductor

bandleader

"BAN"-D TOGETHER

Each clue below suggests a word that begins with the letters B-A-N. See how many you can do on your own. Then band together with a friend if you need help.

1.   A fruit   _____

2.   A group   _____

3.   Covering for a cut   _____

4.   A robber   _____

5.   Loud noise   _____

6.   An instrument   _____

7.   Stair rail   _____

8.   A sign on cloth   _____

9.   Broke   _____

10. Large meal   _____

11. A financial institution   _____

12. An orchestra's platform   _____

13. To expel   _____

14. A tropical tree   _____

15. Destructive   _____

16. A type of chicken   _____

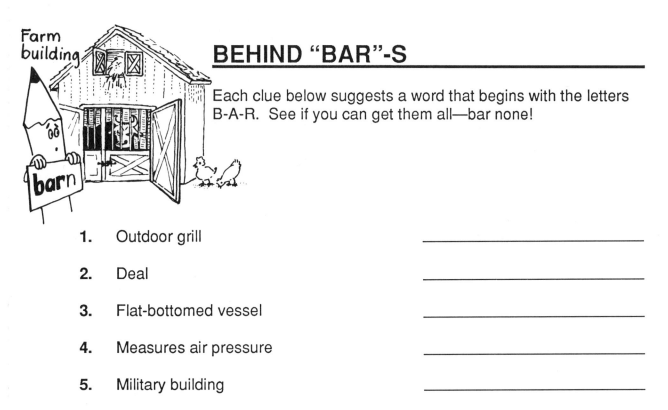

Farm building

BEHIND "BAR"-S

Each clue below suggests a word that begins with the letters B-A-R. See if you can get them all—bar none!

1. Outdoor grill _____

2. Deal _____

3. Flat-bottomed vessel _____

4. Measures air pressure _____

5. Military building _____

6. Ferocious fish _____

7. Empty _____

8. Cylindrical container _____

9. To speak sharply _____

10. To exchange goods _____

11. A weightlifter's equipment _____

12. An occupation _____

13. A Jewish ceremony _____

14. A grain _____

15. A hard-shelled sea creature _____

16. A blockade _____

SHOOT THE "BULL"

Each clue below suggests a word that begins with the letters B-U-L-L. See how many you can do. The first one has been done as an example.

1. A tractor-like machine   _BULLDOZER_

2. A deadly piece of metal   _____

3. A written announcement   _____

4. The center of a target   _____

5. An amphibian   _____

6. A songbird   _____

7. Push around   _____

8. Gold or silver bars   _____

9. Stubborn   _____

10. Spanish entertainment   _____

11. A canine breed   _____

12. A freshwater fish   _____

13. An electric megaphone   _____

14. Where pitchers warm up   _____

Honesty, frankness

You're dull.

candor

I THINK I "CAN"

Each clue below suggests a word that begins with the letters C-A-N. Can you get them all?

1. A songbird _____

2. To take back or withdraw _____

3. A disease _____

4. Very honest _____

5. A waterway _____

6. A walking stick _____

7. A kitchen container _____

8. Small boat _____

9. Holds drinking water _____

10. An overhanging shelter _____

11. A lamp with several lights _____

12. One who runs in an election _____

13. Shrewd _____

14. A wax taper _____

15. A dog _____

16. Type of melon _____

17. A horse's gait _____

18. Coarse, strong fabric _____

19. A deep valley _____

20. An artillery piece _____

Cardboard box

carton

pencils

"CAR" RACING

Each clue below suggests a word that begins with the letters C-A-R. See how many you can do. Get them all, and maybe you'll win a car. (Then again, maybe not.)

1. To be concerned _____

2. A chewy candy _____

3. A large group traveling together _____

4. The dead body of an animal _____

5. Colorful bird _____

6. Cautious _____

7. To rub gently _____

8. One's occupation _____

9. Shipment _____

10. Seasonal songs _____

11. Traveling amusement park _____

12. A woodworker's job _____

13. A rug _____

14. Saturday morning shows _____

15. To transport by hand _____

16. Sent on birthdays _____

17. Vegetable _____

18. Flower _____

19. What most of your ear is made of _____

20. An acrobatic stunt _____

To twist into a strained shape

con**tort**

UNDER "CON"-TROL

Each clue below suggests a word that begins with the letters C-O-N. See how many you can do. Keep your wild guesses under control!

1.   Hide   _____

2.   Accept as true   _____

3.   Think hard   _____

4.   Music performance   _____

5.   Finish   _____

6.   A building material   _____

7.   Railway employee   _____

8.   Rebels in the U.S. Civil War   _____

9.   Meeting   _____

10. Admit   _____

11. Mix up   _____

12. Governmental body   _____

13. To defeat   _____

14. Save   _____

15. Offer sympathy to   _____

16. Large group of vehicles   _____

17. Peacefully happy   _____

18. To join together   _____

19. Always   _____

20. To give thought to   _____

Unafraid

fearless

H-"EAR" ME OUT

Each clue below suggests a word that contains the consecutive letters E-A-R. See how many you can figure out. Do your best—you hear?

1. A sharp weapon _____

2. A pump in your body _____

3. Planet _____

4. Sea gem _____

5. Tired _____

6. An ursine animal _____

7. Vanish _____

8. Equipment _____

9. Tremor _____

10. Facial hair _____

11. Gloomy _____

12. To obtain knowledge _____

13. To acquire by labor _____

14. Full of fright _____

A ring of leaves or flowers

wr**ea**th

"EAT" YOUR WORDS

Each clue below suggests a word that contains the consecutive letters E-A-T. See how many you can do. Get them all, and you won't have to eat them.

1.   A peace agreement   _____

2.   To say over   _____

3.   To inhale and exhale   _____

4.   Below   _____

5.   Warning   _____

6.   A grassy plant   _____

7.   Withdraw   _____

8.   A great deed   _____

9.   A cardigan   _____

10. Part of a bird's covering _____

11. To perspire   _____

12. Atmospheric conditions   _____

13. An animal or human being   _____

14. Win victory over   _____

15. The skin of an animal   _____

A symbolic expression

$a^2 + b^2 = c^2$
$2\pi r = c$
$E = mc^2$

formula

"FOR" BETTER OR WORSE

Each clue below suggests a word that begins with the letters F-O-R. For better or worse, try to do them all.

1. Prohibit _____

2. Weather prediction _____

3. Found on your hand _____

4. A shot in tennis _____

5. An alien person _____

6. Tree-filled area _____

7. Always _____

8. Fail to remember _____

9. Pardon _____

10. Utensil _____

11. Shape _____

12. Riches _____

13. Building occupied by soldiers _____

14. Position in basketball _____

15. To lose a turn _____

To feel great delight

rejoice

COLD AS "ICE"

Each clue below suggests a word that ends with the letters
I-C-E. See how many you can do.

1.   A starchy, edible seed   _____

2.   Counsel   _____

3.   Repeated exercise   _____

4.   Cost   _____

5.   Rodents   _____

6.   Liquid from fruit   _____

7.   Two times   _____

8.   Pleasant   _____

9.   Thin piece   _____

10. Preference   _____

11. Seasoning   _____

12. Used for singing   _____

13. Crime stoppers   _____

14. Blood-sucking insects   _____

15. Marked cubes   _____

To say something rude

Hey, Pencilneck!

insult

"IN" EVERYTHING

Each clue below suggests a word that begins with the letters I-N. See how many you can do. It's IN your best interests to get them all.

1. Mentally ill   _____

2. Cutting teeth   _____

3. Not finished   _____

4. Freedom   _____

5. Unbelievable   _____

6. Make or become greater   _____

7. Very small child   _____

8. Sweet-smelling substance   _____

9. Without a backbone   _____

10. Not guilty   _____

11. Inflamed   _____

12. Each separate person   _____

13. Ask   _____

14. Create   _____

15. Often a pest   _____

16. Smart   _____

17. To fill with air   _____

18. Keeps heat in   _____

19. Immediate   _____

20. Makes music   _____

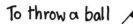

To throw a ball

pitch

YOU CAN DO "IT"

Each clue below suggests a word that contains the letters I-T. Try to get them all. You can do it!

1. A type of bread — — — — — I T

2. Confidence — — I T —

3. Metric measure — I T — —

4. Essay — — — — — — I T — — —

5. To permit to enter — — — I T

6. Cooking room — I T — — — —

7. Jug — I T — — — —

8. What you like best — — — — — — I T —

9. Member of a country — I T — — — —

10. Feelings and behavior — — — I T — — —

11. Maximum amount — — — I T

12. Enthusiasm — — — I T — — — — —

13. Written laws — — — — — I T — — — —

14. Replacement — — — — — I T — — —

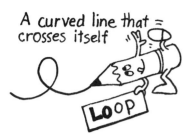

A curved line that crosses itself — LOOP

"LO" AND BEHOLD

Each clue below suggests a word that begins with the letters
L-O. Do your best. Lo and behold, you may get them all!

1. To find   _____

2. To do nothing   _____

3. Part of your ear   _____

4. Money borrowed   _____

5. Crustacean   _____

6. Latch   _____

7. Object worn on a necklace   _____

8. Train engine   _____

9. Cough drop   _____

10. Without company   _____

11. To gaze at   _____

12. Beaver's home   _____

13. Raucous   _____

14. Skin cream   _____

15. Diving bird   _____

16. Faithful   _____

17. Not tightly set   _____

18. Insect like a grasshopper   _____

To fall sharply

plummet

"M & M"S

Each clue below suggests a word that contains the double consonant M. If you get them all, buy yourself some M & Ms—or the treat of your choice.

1. Ventriloquist's friend — — M M —

2. Not acting your age — M M — — — — —

3. Season — — M M — —

4. Order — — M M — — —

5. A musician — — — M M — — —

6. Class of vertebrates — — M M — —

7. Without delay — M M — — — — — —

8. Big — M M — — — —

9. Advertisement on TV — — M M — — — — —

10. Rules for speaking correctly — — — M M — —

11. To begin — — M M — — — —

12. Remark — — M M — — —

13. Disturbance — — M M — — — — —

14. Punctuation mark — — M M —

15. People living in a certain area — — M M — — — — —

16. A strong-smelling liquid or gas — M M — — — —

ONE "PER" WORD

Each clue below suggests a word that contains the consecutive letters P-E-R. See how many you can do. Score one point per word.

1. Part of a car   _____

2. Ruler   _____

3. To allow   _____

4. Phone helper   _____

5. Seasoning   _____

6. Fish   _____

7. Fragrance   _____

8. Footwear   _____

9. A large store   _____

10. Human being   _____

11. Something read daily   _____

12. To act   _____

13. Thermometer reading   _____

14. Building   _____

15. Punctuation mark   _____

16. A good conductor   _____

Animal that pulls a famous sleigh

reindeer

"R & R"

Each clue below suggests a word that begins and ends with the letter R. Get them all, and you'll have earned some R & R!

1. Cools a car's engine _____

2. Roof support _____

3. Poisonous snake _____

4. Back _____

5. Used to shave with _____

6. Gun _____

7. A body of water _____

8. Leftover _____

9. Shaped like an index card _____

10. A morning bird _____

11. List of names _____

12. A measuring device _____

13. A type of chair _____

14. A steering device _____

15. Recall _____

16. Fix _____

17. A farm machine _____

18. To sign up _____

19. Works in a forest preserve _____

20. A lion's call _____

One who performs alone

soloist

"SO" WHAT?

Each clue below suggests a word that begins with the letters S-O. So you can't get them all. So at least you do your best, right?

1.   A sport   _____

2.   Cleaning substance   _____

3.   To find an answer to   _____

4.   Wide-brimmed hat   _____

5.   Like a lemon   _____

6.   Female hog   _____

7.   Dirt   _____

8.   Military person   _____

9.   Outlet   _____

10. Worn on your feet   _____

11. Pop   _____

12. Piece of furniture   _____

13. Wet   _____

14. A liquid food   _____

15. Card game   _____

16. Bottom of shoe   _____

17. From the sun   _____

18. To flip over   _____

19. To separate by type   _____

20. A direction   _____

Part of a climbing plant

tendril

TOP "TEN"

Each clue below suggests a word that contains the consecutive letters T-E-N. Don't stop with the top ten— try for all fifteen!

1.   A sport   _____

2.   Nervous   _____

3.   Outdoor dwelling   _____

4.   A squid's arms   _____

5.   Cords in your body   _____

6.   Delicate   _____

7.   Decayed   _____

8.   To make believe   _____

9.   Many times   _____

10. Satisfied   _____

11. Baby feline   _____

12. To look after   _____

13. An apartment dweller   _____

14. Hand covering   _____

15. A kitchen implement   _____

"UNDER" WHERE?

A dangerous current along the seashore

Each clue below suggests a word that begins with the smaller word UNDER. This one is a real undertaking!

1.   Not old enough   _____

2.   Where deodorant is applied   _____

3.   Not heavy enough   _____

4.   To comprehend   _____

5.   Type of pitch   _____

6.   The team expected to lose   _____

7.   Works at a funeral home   _____

8.   Working secretly   _____

9.   Dig out the earth beneath   _____

10. Where oil is found   _____

11. Mark a word for emphasis   _____

12. To experience   _____

13. A substitute actor or actress   _____

14. Shrubs in a forest   _____

15. Where belugas are found   _____

COMMON COMPOUNDS I

For each group of words below, find a common four-letter word that can be placed in front of the group to make them all compound terms.

Example: <u>BASE</u>
    BALL
    LINE
    HIT

1. _____
    DUST
    BRICK
    RUSH

2. _____
    COLLAR
    GRASS
    PRINT

3. _____
    FRY
    STICK
    BOWL

4. _____
    PINT
    NOTE
    WAY

5. _____
    END
    MARK
    WORM

6. _____
    BLOCK
    HOG
    RUNNER

7. _____
    CHUCK
    WORK
    WIND

8. _____
    BAG
    STONE
    STORM

9. _____
    KNIFE
    POT
    HAMMER

10. _____
    BOWL
    PAN
    DEVIL

COMMON COMPOUNDS II

For each group of words below, find a common four-letter word that can be placed in front of the group to make them all compound terms.

Example: __RAIN__   BOW
                           COAT
                           DROP

1. _____   POUR / WIND / GRADE

2. _____   DUCK / LINE / WEIGHT

3. _____   LIGHT / PRINT / REST

4. _____   PHONE / SET / STRONG

5. _____   MARK / MINE / OWNER

6. _____   OUT / OFF / SOME

7. _____   MAN / STEP / WAY

8. _____   TALK / FIRE / BOARD

9. _____   LINE / PIECE / PIN

10. _____   BOX / HORN / LACE

COMPOUND ADDITION I

The object of this activity is to think of as many words as possible that can be placed after the key word to form a compound term. See if you are sharp enough to fill in all the blanks.

Example: ANY _BODY_ _MORE_
WHERE _PLACE_
HOW _TIME_
THING _WAY_
ONE

1. BED _____

2. FINGER _____

3. BIRTH _____

4. FLASH _____

5. SEA _____

6. HOME _____

COMPOUND ADDITION II

The object of this activity is to think of as many words as possible that can be placed after the key word to form a compound term. See if you are sharp enough to fill in all the blanks.

1. BLUE   _____

      _____

      _____

      _____

      _____

2. SIDE   _____

      _____

      _____

      _____

      _____

3. BLACK _____

      _____

      _____

      _____

      _____

4. SNOW   _____

      _____

      _____

      _____

      _____

5. HOUSE _____

      _____

      _____

      _____

6. SAND   _____

      _____

      _____

      _____

FIRE
+ CRACKER
BANG!

COMPOUND ADDITION III

The object of this activity is to think of as many words as possible that can be placed after the key word to form a compound term. See if you are sharp enough to fill in all the blanks.

1. FIRE _____

_____

_____

_____

_____

_____

_____

_____

_____

2. OUT _____

_____

_____

_____

_____

_____

_____

_____

_____

3. SUN _____

_____

_____

_____

_____

_____

_____

_____

_____

4. WATER _____

_____

_____

_____

_____

_____

_____

_____

_____

SUPER COMPOUND ADDITION

There are more than fifty words that can be placed after the word OVER to make compound words. Can you think of just twenty? How many more can you list?

I've been **over**worked!

OVER _____   _____

_____   _____

_____   _____

_____   _____

_____   _____

_____   _____

_____   _____

_____   _____

_____   _____

_____   _____

BONUS LIST

_____   _____

_____   _____

_____   _____

_____   _____

_____   _____

_____   _____

_____   _____

_____   _____

_____   _____

PENCIL PERFECT POET
PATIENT PROLIFIC

They all start with P... and they all describe me!

HOUSE OF COMMONS I

Each set of words below is grouped together because the words all have something in common. Are you sharp enough to find out what it is? Can you find more than one reason?

Group 1

DEAD   RETREAT   CREATURE   SOAK   TOAD

Answer:

Group 2

TICKET   NOTION   ALABAMA   SCISSORS   ROOSTER

Answer:

Group 3

ALARM   HONOR   CLEVER   BREEZE   DOORKNOB

Answer:

Group 4

MARKET   BILLION   PRAY   SKIM   TIMID

Answer:

Group 5

TRIPLE   CAREER   BUTTON   FORWARD   SINK

Answer:

something about those vowels...

BANANA
KEEPER
CIVILITY
COCOON
USUFRUCT

HOUSE OF COMMONS II

Each set of words below is grouped together because the words all have something in common. Are you sharp enough to find out what it is? Can you find more than one reason?

Group 1

ACTION   TACK   BARRACKS   FRACTION   CADILLAC

Answer:

Group 2

EIGHT   CENT   FLEA   MAIL   SUNDAE

Answer:

Group 3

CONTENT   LIVE   READ   WIND   LEAD

Answer:

Group 4

ROBOT   MOTEL   OPEN   RECESS   REFUND

Answer:

Group 5

TOMB   SOLEMN   ISLAND   GNAW   KNOW

Answer:

OPENING
SPEND
HAPPEN
DEPEND
PENNY

I see my name in each one!

HOUSE OF COMMONS III

Each set of words below is grouped together because the words all have something in common. Are you sharp enough to find out what it is? Can you find more than one reason?

Group 1

WERE	THINK	WALK	WRITE	WORK

Answer:

Group 2

OFTEN	ALONE	HEIGHT	SIXTH	TWOSOME

Answer:

Group 3

FARMER	FEARLESS	SLIP	HANDLE	NECKLACE

Answer:

Group 4

SALT	SUGAR	FLOUR	MILK	SNOW

Answer:

Group 5

FLOCK	PACK	HERD	COLONY	LITTER

Answer:

SCRAMBLED EGGS I

Read each set of clues below. After figuring out the first word, just rearrange its letters to form the second word.

Example: A sack ___BAG___   To talk a lot ___GAB___

1.   Early morning _____   Magician's stick _____

2.   An agreement _____   To be ahead _____

3.   Curved roof _____   A popular style _____

4.   Domestic animal _____   Coastline _____

5.   Gain by working _____   Close by _____

6.   Face covering _____   Not good _____

7.   Part of body _____   A small diner _____

8.   Wild animal _____   To move along _____

9.   An insect _____   A strong taste _____

10.   To listen to _____   A rabbit _____

11.   Rubber tube _____   Footwear _____

12.   A seasoning _____   Final _____

13.   Tardy _____   A story _____

14.   Citrus fruit _____   A distance _____

15.   Implement _____   Slang for money _____

SCRAMBLED EGGS II

Read each set of clues below. After figuring out the first word, just rearrange its letters to form the second word.

Example: Spinning toy __TOP__   Cooking vessel __POT__

1. A fruit _____   A bump _____

2. What you're known by _____   Horse hair _____

3. A companion _____   Domesticated _____

4. A smell _____   An entrance _____

5. To stare at _____   Leaf of a book _____

6. Lacking color _____   To hop _____

7. Part of a hand _____   Light fixture _____

8. A pillar _____   A stain _____

9. Stinging insect _____   Animal feet _____

10. A fruit _____   To cut grain _____

11. Stopper _____   Large swallow _____

12. Strong cord _____   Found in your skin _____

13. To show concern _____   Running contest _____

14. Great anger _____   Equipment _____

15. To rotate _____   A too-small animal _____

SCRAMBLED EGGS III

Read each set of clues below. After figuring out the first word, just rearrange its letters to form the second word.

Example: A vegetable __PEA__   A primate __APE__

1. Long, thin stem _____   Carries blood _____

2. A smile _____   Piece of jewelry _____

3. To run and play _____   High-school dance _____

4. Aching _____   A flower _____

5. Alike _____   Line made by sewing _____

6. To salvage _____   Ornamental jar _____

7. To slide _____   Slang for children _____

8. Written message _____   Quality of sound _____

9. Walking stick _____   Pimples _____

10. To boast _____   To take rapidly _____

11. A clue _____   Narrow _____

12. Part of face _____   To slide suddenly _____

13. A stair _____   Domesticated animals _____

14. Without a covering _____   An animal _____

15. A snare _____   Small portion of _____

WORDS WITHIN WORDS I

Read the clues following each long medical word below. You can find the answers by looking forward or backward in the long word. You cannot skip over any letters or rearrange them in any way. The first one has been done as an example.

Part A.　INTRADERMOREACTION

1.　To move quickly　　　　　DART

2.　Word meaning "exchange"

3.　Great paintings

4.　A hue

5.　A pronoun

6.　A negative

7.　Word meaning "excess"

8.　Source of iron

9.　Respond

10.　Division of a play

Part B.　BARRANDEOCERATIDA

1.　A verb of being

2.　A rodent

3.　An action verb

4.　A sticky substance

5.　Word meaning "exclude"

6.　A connecting word

7.　A commercial

WORDS WITHIN WORDS II

Read the clues following each long medical word below. You can find the answers by looking forward or backward in the long word. You cannot skip over any letters or rearrange them in any way. The first one has been done as an example.

Part A.   HEPATONEPHROMEGALY

1.   An objective pronoun   <u>ME</u>

2.   A subjective pronoun   _____

3.   A single unit   _____

4.   A measure of weight   _____

5.   Writing device   _____

6.   A city in Italy   _____

7.   A precious stone   _____

8.   Greek word meaning "the end"   _____

9.   Quality of sound   _____

10.   To grow old   _____

Part B.   BELLEROPHONTACEA

1.   Near or by   _____

2.   Found on skin   _____

3.   A negative   _____

4.   A feline   _____

5.   Not off   _____

6.   Has a clapper   _____

7.   A playing card   _____

WORDS WITHIN WORDS III

Read the clues following each long medical word below. You can find the answers by looking forward or backward in the word. You cannot skip over any letters or rearrange them in any way. The first one has been done as an example.

Part A.   CHEILOGNATHOPALATOSCHISIS

1. A subjective pronoun   _HE_

2. A large piece of wood   _____

3. A sharp taste   _____

4. An insect   _____

5. A verb of being   _____

6. To fib   _____

7. A colorful stone   _____

8. Word that shows possession   _____

9. A color   _____

10. A ballroom dance   _____

Part B.   POLIOENCEPHALOMENINGOMYELITIS

1. A ring of light   _____

2. A number   _____

3. A fuel   _____

4. Floor covering   _____

5. A warning   _____

6. A possessive pronoun   _____

7. To chop off   _____

By reading either clockwise or counterclockwise, you will find a commonly used eight-letter word in each circle below. After finding the word, tell whether it is a noun, verb, adjective, adverb, or pronoun. The first one has been done as an example.

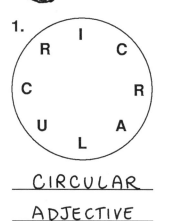

1.

CIRCULAR

ADJECTIVE

2.

_____

_____

3.

_____

_____

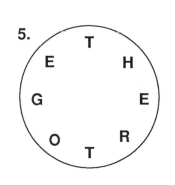

4.

_____

_____

5.

_____

_____

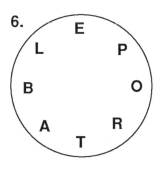

6.

_____

_____

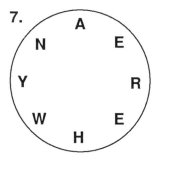

7.

_____

_____

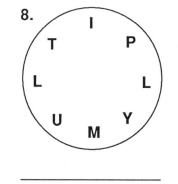

8.

_____

_____

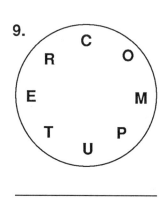

9.

_____

_____

AROUND THE WORLD II

By reading either clockwise or counterclockwise, you will find a commonly used eight-letter word in each circle below. After finding the word, tell whether it is a noun, verb, adjective, adverb, or pronoun.

1.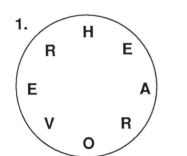

_____

_____

2.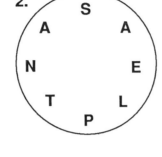

_____

_____

3.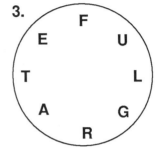

_____

_____

4.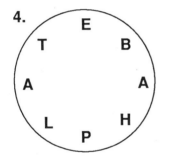

_____

_____

5.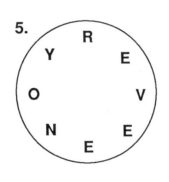

_____

_____

6.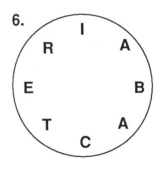

_____

_____

7.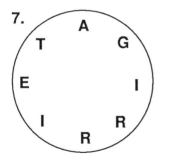

_____

_____

8.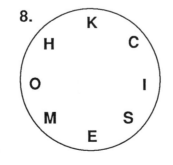

_____

_____

9.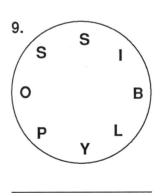

_____

_____

AROUND THE WORLD III

By reading either clockwise or counterclockwise, you will find a commonly used eight-letter word in each circle below. After finding the word, tell whether it is a noun, verb, adjective, adverb, or pronoun.

1.
```
      Y
  S       H
 I         P
  C       L
      A
```
_____
_____

2.
```
      M
  E       O
 V         H
  E       W
      R
```
_____
_____

3.
```
      M
  A       U
 Q         I
  U       R
      A
```
_____
_____

4.
```
      T
  E       I
 M         M
  O       E
      S
```
_____
_____

5.
```
      B
  I       E
 R         D
  C       E
      S
```
_____
_____

6.
```
      I
  S       N
 R         G
  A       U
      L
```
_____
_____

7.
```
      O
  L       P
 I         Y
  T       L
      E
```
_____
_____

8.
```
      D
  Y       O
 S         B
  O       E
      M
```
_____
_____

9.
```
      N
  E       L
 D         Y
  D       S
      U
```
_____
_____

CONTRACTION SEARCH

A contraction is a shortened form of a word or phrase. The words that make up the contractions listed below are hidden in the puzzle. They can be found reading up, down, forward, or backward. Circle each word group you find in the puzzle and write it next to the corresponding contraction. The first one has been done as an example.

```
B O S D A R Y S M N W
A S W E A R E H T I C
R T W E H A V E F G H
T O R B E T D I T I S
O N C C I O F S H H O
N D P A S N O N E P M
O L J N F E E D Y L T
D U L N S V G O H R V
R O Y O U A R E A C U
U H K T U H I S V B A
D S B H J I L N E D G
T O N E R A G O U J L
S W T Y W O E T E U L
Y O U W I L L I V G I
P L D I A M O E W S W
W I L L N O T R O P E
I K J L T O N S A W H
```

1. AREN'T   ARE NOT
2. CAN'T _____
3. DOESN'T _____
4. DON'T_____
5. HAVEN'T _____
6. HE'LL _____
7. HE'S _____
8. I'M _____
9. IT'S _____
10. I'VE _____
11. SHE'S _____
12. SHOULDN'T_____
13. THEY'LL _____
14. THEY'VE _____
15. WASN'T _____
16. WE'RE _____
17. WE'VE _____
18. WON'T _____
19. YOU'LL _____
20. YOU'RE _____

HOMOPHONE SEARCH

A homophone is a word that sounds like another word but has a different spelling and meaning. The homophones of the words listed below are hidden in the puzzle. They can be found reading up, down, forward, or backward. Circle each word you find in the puzzle and write it next to the corresponding homophone. The first one has been done as an example.

```
P  O  S  D  A  R  Y  S  M  N  W
R  A  T  E  D  I  K  J  L  M  T
I  N  P  L  E  W  A  S  N  A  O
N  T  D  I  L  A  M  O  E  L  N
T  I  V  E  L  O  H  G  I  E  K
S  L  L  W  I  I  U  U  O  B  W
W  T  S  K  B  E  R  R  Y  N  G
N  L  G  R  E  B  K  N  O  W  S
V  U  C  G  A  J  M  P  R  O  V
R  O  W  S  T  S  T  I  D  R  T
O  F  E  R  E  E  L  F  B  H  R
T  N  S  I  G  I  H  P  L  T  I
H  T  R  U  O  F  R  C  B  D  A
J  U  A  G  S  P  W  A  O  W  T
V  E  O  U  E  H  Y  M  N  V  S
A  H  H  Y  E  T  F  T  O  M  W
Y  K  L  I  O  G  E  O  T  N  Y
```

1. AUNT _____ANT_____
2. EIGHT _____
3. BUILD _____
4. BURY _____
5. BEET _____
6. EARN _____
7. FOWL _____
8. FLEA _____
9. FORTH _____
10. HIM _____
11. HORSE _____
12. NOT _____
13. WHOLE _____
14. NOSE _____
15. MAIL _____
16. PRINCE _____
17. ROSE _____
18. STARE _____
19. THRONE _____
20. TOW _____

ACTION VERB SEARCH

An action verb is a word that describes an action. The puzzle below contains 20 commonly used action verbs. The first letter of each one has been provided for you. The verbs can be found reading up, down, forward, or backward. Find each verb and complete its spelling to the right of the appropriate letter. The first one has been done as an example.

```
B  L  A  E  H  U  K  E  E  P  N
O  D  K  S  I  N  G  O  S  M  O
S  E (A  V  O  I  D) T  Q  U  N
D  N  W  N  D  L  I  W  J  J  I
A  I  O  J  Y  A  C  E  D  A  A
R  G  K  W  T  U  B  J  M  C  T
C  A  R  R  Y  G  N  E  A  P  B
O  M  A  F  G  H  R  C  G  I  O
N  I  B  B  L  E  E  T  N  C  T
T  E  A  S  E  M  V  H  I  K  I
R  N  F  O  L  L  O  W  F  L  U
T  A  E  P  E  R  G  I  Y  M  Q
```

Be careful! You may find words in the puzzle that are **not** action verbs.

1. A V O I D _____
2. B _____
3. C _____
4. D _____
5. E _____
6. F _____
7. G _____
8. H _____
9. I _____
10. J _____
11. K _____
12. L _____
13. M _____
14. N _____
15. O _____
16. P _____
17. Q _____
18. R _____
19. S _____
20. T _____

ADJECTIVE SEARCH

An adjective is a word that describes or modifies a noun. The puzzle below contains 20 commonly used adjectives. Circle each adjective you find and write it on one of the lines to the right. Words can be found reading up, down, forward, or backward. One has been done as an example.

```
P  W  O  B  B  L  Y  E  R  E
U  S  L  E  H  W  T  M  E  A
R  S  D  I  O  D  S  P  B  T
P  T  I  N  Y  E  A  T  L  W
L  N  Y  E  T  D  T  Y  U  E
E  H  O  U  L  A  R  G  E  A
E  D  I  W  Y  F  N  S  H  R
L  P  L  O  E  S  I  L  L  Y
T  R  D  O  L  P  H  Y  M  N
N  A  G  D  L  Y  T  S  U  D
E  H  F  E  O  K  S  A  M  P
G  S  J  N  W  T  L  E  R  O
D  E  L  I  G  H  T  F  U  L
```

1. ___BLUE___
2. _____
3. _____
4. _____
5. _____
6. _____
7. _____
8. _____
9. _____
10. _____
11. _____
12. _____
13. _____
14. _____
15. _____
16. _____
17. _____
18. _____
19. _____
20. _____

Be careful! You may find words in the puzzle that are **not** adjectives.

ADVERB SEARCH

An adverb modifies a verb by telling **when, where,** or **how**.
Hidden in this puzzle are 20 adverbs. The words can be found
reading up, down, forward, or backward. See how many you
can find. Write each adverb in the appropriate list. One has
been done as an example.

Reluctantly...

```
T E A R L Y G I F T E N
C Y N C S L O L P H E E
D I Y A O A L A M E R N
A N W A O C K Z D N E E
I C H T N I O I N E H A
Y A E R E T A L T T W T
L B R A V E L Y H F E L
W Y E R E H C O E O M Y
O L O N B N E H R E O R
L P N O W H E R E E S S
S F U W C Q U I C K L Y
Y L I P P A H K V I L D
C A P R A L W A Y S S A
Y L L U F T H G I L E D
T E V E R Y W H E R E A
```

Be careful! You may find words in the
puzzle that are **not** adverbs.

Hint: Many adverbs that
tell **how** end in -LY.

When

1. ___ALWAYS___
2. _____
3. _____
4. _____
5. _____
6. _____
7. _____

Where

1. _____
2. _____
3. _____
4. _____
5. _____
6. _____

How

1. _____
2. _____
3. _____
4. _____
5. _____
6. _____
7. _____

PRONOUN SEARCH

A pronoun takes the place of a noun or nouns in a sentence. Hidden in this puzzle are 26 pronouns—12 **personal** pronouns, 8 **reflexive** pronouns, and 6 **relative** or **interrogative** pronouns. The words can be found reading up, down, forward, or backward. See how many you can find. Write each pronoun in the appropriate list. One has been done as an example.

```
F  L  E  S  R  E  H (H  E) N  W  D
T  A  H  T  I  N  S  I  A  P  H  T
A  B  V  S  I  U  H  M  F  L  A  H
T  R  I  W  H  O  O  Y  L  S  T  E
W  E  S  T  R  Y  P  S  E  E  W  M
S  H  E  M  D  K  L  E  S  V  H  S
U  S  N  U  T  W  O  L  R  L  O  E
W  O  D  T  H  E  Y  F  U  E  S  L
H  I  M  S  E  L  F  G  O  S  E  V
I  M  A  N  M  K  P  O  Y  R  D  E
C  J  S  E  V  L  E  S  R  U  O  S
H  I  T  S  E  L  F  N  M  O  H  W
O  C  T  D  E  C  J  A  N  Y  F  E
```

Personal Pronouns

1. __HE__   7. _____
2. _____   8. _____
3. _____   9. _____
4. _____   10. _____
5. _____   11. _____
6. _____   12. _____

Reflexive Pronouns

1. _____   5. _____
2. _____   6. _____
3. _____   7. _____
4. _____   8. _____

Be careful! You may find words in the puzzle that are **not** pronouns.

Hint: Use an English or grammar book if you need help in figuring out the types of pronouns.

Relative or Interrogative Pronouns

1. _____   4. _____
2. _____   5. _____
3. _____   6. _____

BOOK ENDS

By rearranging the letters in only the first and last three-letter groups, you can discover a commonly used nine-letter word.

Example: RAP **CTI** ALC   <u>PRACTICAL</u>

1. ARC **DBO** RAD   _____

2. ERP **MIT** ETD   _____

3. VAD **ERT** SIE   _____

4. ONC **TIN** TEN   _____

5. AND **GER** USO   _____

6. OIP **SON** SUO   _____

7. ENC **ESS** RAY   _____

8. PED **ART** RUE   _____

9. UCO **RTE** UOS   _____

10. USC **TOM** YAR   _____

11. LOP **LUT** OIN   _____

12. VAD **ANT** GEA   _____

13. LET **ESC** POE   _____

14. ANC **DID** AET   _____

15. NOC **STR** CUT   _____

16. VEA **POR** TAE   _____

17. POE **RAT** NIO   _____

18. CRO **HES** RAT   _____

19. HET **REF** OER   _____

20. ORS **ROW** FLU   _____

WANT ADS

JOB HUNTING

By rearranging each three-letter group correctly, you will have a nine-letter word that names a type of job or occupation.

Example: USC ODT NAI _CUSTODIAN_

1. FIL GEU RAD _____
2. TSA ONR UAT _____
3. TED CET EVI _____
4. ARC NEP RTE _____
5. ESC ERT RAY _____
6. HPY ICS NIA _____
7. COE OLG SIT _____
8. PER IDS TEN _____
9. RAC TIH TEC _____
10. ROP FSE OSR _____
11. OCU SEN ORL _____
12. RIP CIN ALP _____
13. ONC CUD ROT _____
14. OIB OGL SIT _____
15. ISC TEN STI _____
16. IBL RRA NIA _____
17. NAN UNO RCE _____
18. BUP SLI RHE _____

A PAIR OF PEARS

The answers to each set of clues below are homophones.

Example: Also ___TOO___   A number ___TWO___

1. Curve _____   Biblical boat _____

2. Insensitive _____   Hardened skin _____

3. To sell _____   Part of a bike _____

4. Pronoun _____   Female sheep _____

5. Flew high _____   Sharp blade _____

6. To rule _____   Precipitation _____

7. Encounter _____   A steak _____

8. Sole _____   Lend _____

9. Church song _____   Objective pronoun _____

10. Quick look _____   Mountaintop _____

11. To take from _____   Oceans _____

12. To make a liquid flow _____   Skin opening _____

13. To stun _____   Time periods _____

14. Run away _____   Insect _____

15. Authentic _____   Winding device _____

16. Vegetable _____   To strike or hit _____

17. Carry _____   Passageway _____

18. Atmosphere _____   Inheritor _____

19. Fibber _____   Musical instrument _____

20. Confusing paths _____   Corn _____

END TO END

By adding one letter before and one letter after each smaller word below, you can make a completely new word. Plurals are not allowed. Some will have more than one answer.

Example: K NO T

1.   ___ WENT ___

2.   ___ OUT ___

3.   ___ LIE ___

4.   ___ TEA ___

5.   ___ US ___

6.   ___ OURS ___

7.   ___ WAR ___

8.   ___ TAG ___

9.   ___ PEN ___

10.   ___ ROPE ___

11.   ___ WIN ___

12.   ___ LANE ___

13.   ___ APE ___

14.   ___ ART ___

15.   ___ EAR ___

16.   ___ CAR ___

17.   ___ RAM ___

18.   ___ BUS ___

19.   ___ EVE ___

20.   ___ AGO ___

21.   ___ OMEN ___

22.   ___ TREE ___

23.   ___ NOW ___

24.   ___ PEA ___

DOUBLE END TO END

By adding two letters to the beginning and two letters to the end of each set of letters below, you can make a familiar word. Clues are given to help you. Plurals are not allowed.

Example: Person who travels   T O U R I S T

1.	Far away	_ _ S T A _ _
2.	To make	_ _ O D U _ _
3.	You drive on this	_ _ G H W _ _
4.	You look up at this	_ _ I L I _ _
5.	You eat this	_ _ T M E _ _
6.	You ride this	_ _ C Y C _ _
7.	Open grassy land	_ _ A I R _ _
8.	Type of store	_ _ O C E _ _
9.	Drapery	_ _ R T A _ _
10.	Versus	_ _ A I N _ _
11.	A room	_ _ T C H _ _
12.	Error	_ _ S T A _ _
13.	Top of the ocean	_ _ R F A _ _
14.	Show reverence for	_ _ R S H _ _
15.	Give your word	_ _ O M I _ _
16.	Envious	_ _ A L O _ _
17.	To seize control of	_ _ P T U _ _
18.	To investigate	_ _ P L O _ _
19.	Stop from happening	_ _ E V E _ _
20.	Maybe	_ _ R H A _ _

ocean
+
male child
=
season

IT ALL ADDS UP

For each pair of clues below, figure out the two words, then add them together to form another word.

Example: Not on + Frozen water = ___OFFICE___

1.   Portable bed + A measure of weight = _____

2.   A rodent + An objective pronoun = _____

3.   A greeting + A tale = _____

4.   Black substance + To obtain = _____

5.   Lower limb + Finish = _____

6.   To exist + To possess = _____

7.   A vehicle + To decay = _____

8.   Objective pronoun + A small insect = _____

9.   A negative + Angry = _____

10.   Body part + Container = _____

11.   Short sleep + Relatives = _____

12.   In favor of + Melody = _____

13.   Subject pronoun + Skill = _____

14.   Achieve victory + Royal figure = _____

15.   Ride the waves + A playing card = _____

DOUBLE UP

Below is a list of double letters. For each letter pair, try to think of at least two words that contain these double letters. Can you think of more?

Example: AA   _AARDVARK_   _BAZAAR_

BONUS

1. BB _____ _____ _____

2. CC _____ _____ _____

3. DD _____ _____ _____

4. EE _____ _____ _____

5. FF _____ _____ _____

6. GG _____ _____ _____

7. KK _____ _____ _____

8. LL _____ _____ _____

9. MM _____ _____ _____

10. NN _____ _____ _____

11. OO _____ _____ _____

12. PP _____ _____ _____

13. RR _____ _____ _____

14. SS _____ _____ _____

15. TT _____ _____ _____

16. ZZ _____ _____ _____

EVOLUTION

The object of this activity is to change a word, one letter at a time, into a new word. Each step in between must also be a word. More than one answer may be possible for each problem.

FUN to PET

FUN
FAN
MAN
MEN
MET
PET

1. HOME to WORK _____

2. FOOT to BALL _____

3. EAST to WEST _____

4. LOVE to HATE _____

5. BOAT to SHIP _____

6. HAND to FOOT _____

7. BOOK to PAGE _____

8. SEAT to DESK _____

9. SOCK to SLOB _____

10. RULE to CARE _____

ANSWERS

Suggested answers are given on these pages; however, many of the problems in this book can have more than one answer. Accept correct student answers even if they differ from the answers given below.

Page 1   Expanding Words
1. ace, pace   2. act, pact   3. ant, pant   4. eagle, beagle   5. eel, reel   6. oral, coral   7. inch, pinch
8. order, border   9. itch, ditch   10. ask, task
11. ouch, couch

Page 2   Vowel Change
1. strong, string   2. wind, wand   3. turn, torn
4. tell, toll   5. slam, slim   6. pitch, patch   7. bowl, bawl   8. chip, chap   9. blink, blank   10. sip, sap
11. seal, soil   12. year, your   13. warm, worm
14. spin, span   15. wash, wish   16. vapor, viper
17. stool, steel   18. rush, rash   19. blend, blind
20. cheer, chair   21. middle, muddle

Page 3   Metamorphosis I
1. ace, are   2. acre, ache   3. battle, bottle
4. board, beard   5. cable, table   6. cage, page
7. truck, trick   8. deal, heal   9. ear, eat
10. faint, paint   11. feast, beast   12. wasp, gasp
13. golf, wolf   14. house, horse   15. jingle, jungle

Page 4   Metamorphosis II
1. judge, fudge   2. knob, snob   3. fork, work
4. lump, limp   5. leaf, deaf   6. mall, male
7. merry, mercy   8. nose, note   9. odd, old
10. parrot, carrot   11. park, pork   12. quick, quack   13. quilt, quill   14. racket, rocket
15. rain, ruin

Page 5   Metamorphosis III
1. sand, said   2. scale, scare   3. tackle, tickle
4. easy, east   5. tender, fender   6. umpire, empire
7. utter, otter   8. van, tan   9. warp, carp
10. waste, taste   11. yawn, fawn   12. wind, find
13. wobble, gobble   14. mink, mine   15. zoo, too

Page 6   "O" No
1. motor   2. color   3. monsoon   4. photo
5. motto   6. voodoo   7. forgot   8. follow
9. bronco   10. school   11. footstool
12. foolproof   13. sorrow   14. tomorrow
15. colon   16. solo   17. hobo   18. robot
19. cocoon   20. colony   21. common
22. convoy   23. odor; door

Page 7   "ACT" It Out
1. factory   2. fact   3. compact   4. extract
5. practice   6. practical   7. contact   8. tractor
9. exactly   10. subtract   11. cactus
12. fraction   13. protractor   14. bacteria

Page 8   What Is Your "AGE"?
1. cabbage   2. shortage   3. luggage; baggage
4. voyage   5. garage   6. courage   7. damage
8. savage   9. sausage   10. postage   11. cage
12. message   13. rage   14. carriage
15. stage   16. village

Page 9   Bet You C-"AN'T"
1. giant   2. elephant   3. anthem   4. fantasy
5. important; significant   6. pant   7. vacant
8. antonym   9. restaurant   10. quantity
11. fragrant   12. distant   13. mantle
14. pleasant

Page 10   "ARE" You Ready?
1. glare   2. square   3. fare   4. scare
5. spare   6. beware   7. parent(s)   8. snare
9. area   10. arena   11. flare   12. aware
13. mare   14. share

Page 11   I "ATE" the Whole Thing
1. imitate   2. irrigate   3. irritate   4. evaporate
5. graduate   6. locate   7. chocolate   8. skate
9. decorate   10. hesitate   11. separate
12. create   13. vertebrate   14. accurate
15. estimate   16. educate   17. crate
18. rotate   19. celebrate   20. operate

Page 12   "BAN"-d Together
1. banana   2. band   3. bandage; Band-Aid
4. bandit   5. bang   6. banjo   7. banister
8. banner   9. bankrupt   10. banquet   11. bank
12. bandstand   13. banish   14. banyan
15. baneful   16. bantam

Page 13   Behind "BAR"-s
1. barbecue   2. bargain   3. barge   4. barometer
5. barracks   6. barracuda   7. barren; bare
8. barrel   9. bark   10. barter   11. barbell
12. barber   13. bar mitzvah   14. barley
15. barnacle   16. barricade

Page 14   Shoot the "BULL"
1. bulldozer   2. bullet   3. bulletin   4. bull's-eye
5. bullfrog   6. bullfinch   7. bully   8. bullion
9. bullheaded   10. bullfight   11. bulldog;
bullmastiff; bullterrier   12. bullhead   13. bullhorn
14. bullpen

Page 15   I Think I "CAN"
1. canary   2. cancel   3. cancer   4. candid
5. canal   6. cane   7. canister   8. canoe
9. canteen   10. canopy   11. candelabra
12. candidate   13. canny   14. candle   15. canine
16. cantaloupe   17. canter   18. canvas
19. canyon   20. cannon

Page 16   "CAR" Racing
1. care   2. caramel   3. caravan   4. carcass;
carrion   5. cardinal   6. careful   7. caress
8. career   9. cargo   10. carols   11. carnival
12. carpentry   13. carpet   14. cartoons
15. carry   16. cards   17. carrot   18. carnation
19. cartilage   20. cartwheel

Page 17   Under "CON"-trol
1. conceal   2. concede   3. concentrate
4. concert   5. conclude   6. concrete
7. conductor   8. confederates   9. conference;
convention; convocation   10. confess   11. confuse
12. congress   13. conquer   14. conserve
15. console   16. convoy   17. content
18. connect   19. constantly; continuously
20. consider

Page 18   H-"EAR" Me Out
1. spear   2. heart   3. earth   4. pearl
5. weary   6. bear   7. disappear   8. gear
9. earthquake   10. beard   11. dreary
12. learn   13. earn   14. fearful

Page 19   "EAT" Your Words
1. treaty   2. repeat   3. breathe   4. beneath
5. threat   6. wheat   7. retreat   8. feat
9. sweater   10. feather   11. sweat
12. weather   13. creature   14. defeat
15. leather

Page 20   "FOR" Better or Worse
1. forbid   2. forecast   3. forefinger   4. forehand
5. foreigner   6. forest   7. forever   8. forget
9. forgive   10. fork   11. form   12. fortune
13. fort   14. forward   15. forfeit

Page 21   Cold as "ICE"
1. rice   2. advice   3. practice   4. price
5. mice   6. juice   7. twice   8. nice   9. slice
10. choice   11. spice   12. voice   13. police
14. lice   15. dice

Page 22   "IN" Everything
1. insane   2. incisors   3. incomplete
4. independence   5. incredible   6. increase
7. infant   8. incense   9. invertebrate
10. innocent   11. infected   12. individual
13. inquire   14. invent   15. insect
16. intelligent; ingenious; intellectual   17. inflate
18. insulation   19. instant   20. instrument

Page 23   You Can Do "IT"
1. biscuit   2. faith   3. liter (litre)   4. composition
5. admit   6. kitchen   7. pitcher   8. favorite
9. citizen   10. attitude   11. limit
12. excitement   13. constitution   14. substitute

Page 24   "LO" and Behold
1. locate   2. loaf   3. lobe   4. loan   5. lobster
6. lock   7. locket   8. locomotive   9. lozenge
10. lonesome; lonely   11. look   12. lodge
13. loud   14. lotion   15. loon   16. loyal
17. loose   18. locust

Page 25   "M & M"s
1. dummy   2. immature   3. summer
4. command   5. drummer   6. mammal
7. immediate   8. immense   9. commercial
10. grammar   11. commence   12. comment
13. commotion   14. comma   15. community
16. ammonia

Page 26   One "PER" Word
1. bumper   2. emperor   3. permit   4. operator
5. pepper   6. perch   7. perfume   8. slipper
9. supermarket   10. person   11. paper;
newspaper   12. perform   13. temperature
14. skyscraper   15. period   16. copper

Page 27   "R & R"
1. radiator   2. rafter   3. rattler   4. rear
5. razor   6. revolver   7. river   8. remainder
9. rectangular   10. rooster   11. roster
12. ruler   13. rocker   14. rudder   15. remember
16. repair   17. reaper; rototiller   18. register
19. ranger   20. roar

Page 28   "SO" What?
1. soccer   2. soap   3. solve   4. sombrero
5. sour   6. sow   7. soil   8. soldier   9. socket
10. socks   11. soda   12. sofa   13. soaked;
soggy   14. soup   15. solitaire   16. sole
17. solar   18. somersault   19. sort   20. south

Page 29   Top "TEN"
1. tennis   2. tense   3. tent   4. tentacles
5. tendons   6. tender   7. rotten   8. pretend
9. often   10. content   11. kitten   12. tend
13. tenant   14. mitten   15. utensil

Page 30   "UNDER" Where?
1. underage   2. underarm   3. underweight
4. understand   5. underhand   6. underdog
7. undertaker   8. undercover   9. undermine
10. underground   11. underline   12. undergo
13. understudy   14. underbrush   15. underwater;
undersea

Page 31   Common Compounds I
1. gold   2. blue   3. fish   4. half   5. book
6. road   7. wood   8. sand   9. jack   10. dust

Page 32   Common Compounds II
1. down   2. dead   3. foot   4. head   5. land
6. hand   7. door   8. back   9. hair   10. shoe

Page 33   Compound Addition I
Answers will vary. Possibilities include: 1. bedroom,
bedtime, bedclothes, bedbug, bedspread   2. fingernail,
fingerprint, fingerpaint, fingertip, fingerboard
3. birthday, birthmark, birthplace, birthstone, birthright
4. flashlight, flashbulb, flashback, flashcube, flash flood
5. seaweed, seacoast, seashell, seashore, seasick
6. homework, hometown, homemade, homesick,
homecoming

Page 34   Compound Addition II
Answers will vary. Possibilities include: 1. bluebird,
bluebell, blueberry, bluegrass, blueprint   2. sidearm,
sidewalk, sideways, sidewinder, sidelines
3. blackbird, blackberry, blackboard, blacksmith,
blackmail   4. snowman, showshoes, snowflake,
snowball, snowmobile   5. housefly, houseboat,
housework, housekeeper, housepainter   6. sandbox,
sandbag, sandpaper, sandstorm, sandman

Page 35   Compound Addition III
Answers will vary. Possibilities include: **1.** firefly,
fireplace, firewood, firefighters, fireplug, fireworks,
firetrap, fireproof, fireball **2.** outbreak, outdoors,
outfield, outgoing, outline, outgrow, outrun, outside, outwit
3. sunset, sunshine, sunburn, sunglasses, sundial,
sunlamp, sunlight, sunstroke, sunbeam **4.** waterfall,
watercolor, watermelon, waterfront, waterlogged,
waterproof, waterski, waterfowl, waterlily

Page 36   Super Compound Addition
Answers will vary. Possibilities include: overact, overalls,
overboard, overcast, overcoat, overcrowd, overdue,
overeat, overflow, overhand, overhead, overjoy, overland,
overload, overlook, overnight, overpass, overseas,
oversleep, overturn

Page 37   House of Commons I
Answers may vary.
Group 1. "A" is silent in each word
Group 2. First and last letters the same
Group 3. One vowel for each word
Group 4. Personal names within words
Group 5. Smaller words within

Page 38   House of Commons II
Answers may vary.
Group 1. All contain "AC"
Group 2. All have homophones
Group 3. Can be pronounced two ways
Group 4. First vowel long, second vowel short
Group 5. Silent letter in each word

Page 39   House of Commons III
Answers may vary.
Group 1. All are verbs
Group 2. Numbers within
Group 3. Body parts within
Group 4. All are white
Group 5. All are group names

Page 40   Scrambled Eggs I
1. dawn, wand **2.** deal, lead **3.** dome, mode
4. horse, shore **5.** earn, near **6.** veil, evil
7. face, cafe **8.** wolf, flow **9.** gnat, tang
10. hear, hare **11.** hose, shoe **12.** salt, last
13. late, tale **14.** lime, mile **15.** tool, loot

Page 41   Scrambled Eggs II
1. plum, lump **2.** name, mane **3.** mate, tame
4. odor, door **5.** gape, page **6.** pale, leap
7. palm, lamp **8.** post, spot **9.** wasp, paws
10. pear, reap **11.** plug, gulp **12.** rope, pore
13. care, race **14.** rage, gear **15.** turn, runt

Page 42   Scrambled Eggs III
1. vine, vein **2.** grin, ring **3.** romp, prom
4. sore, rose **5.** same, seam **6.** save, vase
7. skid, kids **8.** note, tone **9.** cane, acne
10. brag, grab **11.** hint, thin **12.** lips, slip
13. step, pets **14.** bare, bear **15.** trap, part

Page 43   Words Within Words I
Part A.   1. dart **2.** trade **3.** art **4.** red
5. it **6.** no **7.** more **8.** ore **9.** react
10. act
Part B.   1. are **2.** rat **3.** ran **4.** tar
5. bar **6.** and **7.** ad

Page 44   Words Within Words II
Part A.   1. me **2.** he **3.** one **4.** ton
5. pen **6.** Rome **7.** gem **8.** omega **9.** tone
10. age
Part B.   1. at **2.** pore **3.** no **4.** cat **5.** on
6. bell **7.** ace

Page 45   Words Within Words III
Part A.   1. he **2.** log **3.** tang **4.** gnat
5. is **6.** lie **7.** opal **8.** his **9.** tan
10. tango
Part B.   1. halo **2.** nine **3.** oil **4.** tile
5. omen **6.** my **7.** lop

Page 46   Around the World I
1. circular—adj. **2.** frontier—n.
3. conserve—v. **4.** yourself—pron. **5.** together—
adv. **6.** portable—adj. **7.** anywhere—adv.
8. multiply—v. **9.** computer—n.

Page 47   Around the World II
1. overhear—v. **2.** pleasant—adj. **3.** grateful—
adj. **4.** alphabet—n. **5.** everyone—pron.
6. bacteria—n. **7.** irrigate—v. **8.** homesick—adj.
9. possibly—adv.

Page 48   Around the World III
1. physical—adj. **2.** whomever—pron.
3. aquarium—n. **4.** sometime—adv.
5. describe—v. **6.** singular—adj. **7.** politely—
adv. **8.** somebody—pron. **9.** suddenly—adv.

Page 49   Contraction Search
1. are not
2. cannot
3. does not
4. do not
5. have not
6. he will
7. he is
8. I am
9. it is
10. I have
11. she is
12. should not
13. they will
14. they have
15. was not
16. we are
17. we have
18. will not
19. you will
20. you are

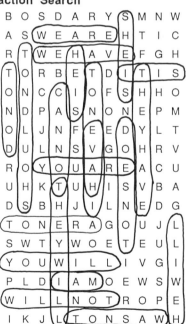

Page 50 — Homophone Search

1. ant
2. ate
3. billed
4. berry
5. beat
6. urn
7. foul
8. flee
9. fourth
10. hymn
11. hoarse
12. knot
13. hole
14. knows
15. male
16. prints
17. rows
18. stair
19. thrown
20. toe

```
P O S D A R Y S M N W
R A T E D I K J L M T
I N P L E W A S N A O
N T D I L A M O E L N
T I V E L O H G I E K
S L L W I I U U O B W
W T S K B E R R Y N G
N L G R E B K N O W S
V U C G A J M P R O V
R O W S T S T I D R T
O F E R E E L F B H R
T N S I G I H P L T I
H T R U O F R C B D A
J U A G S P W A O W T
V E O U E H Y M N V S
A H H Y E T F T O M W
Y K L I O G E O T N Y
```

Page 51 — Action Verb Search

1. avoid
2. bark
3. carry
4. decay
5. eject
6. follow
7. govern
8. hoal
9. imagine
10. jump
11. keep
12. laugh
13. make
14. nibble
15. obtain
16. pick
17. quit
18. repeat
19. sing
20. tease

```
B L A E H U K E E P N
O D K S I N G O S M O
S E A V O I D T Q U N
D N W N D L I W I J I
A I O J Y A C E D A A
R G K W T U B J M C T
C A R R Y G N E A P B
O M A F G H R C G I O
N I B B L E E T N C T
T E A S E M V H I K I
R N F O L L O W F L U
T A E P E R G I Y M Q
```

Page 52 — Adjective Search

NOTE: Answers may be in any order.

blue
delightful
dusty
easy
empty
faded
gentle
large
old
purple
sharp
silly
tasty
thin
tiny
weary
wide
wobbly
wooden
yellow

```
P W O B B L Y E R E
U S L E H W T M E A
R S D I O D S P B T
P T I N Y E A T L W
L N Y E T D T Y U E
E H O U L A R G E A
E D I W Y F N S H R
L P L O E S I L L Y
T R D O L P H Y M N
N A G D L Y T S U D
E H F E O K S A M P
G S J N W T L E R O
D E L I G H T F U L
```

Page 53 — Adverb Search

NOTE: Answers within each category may be in any order.

When
always
early
later
now
often
soon
then

Where
anywhere
everywhere
here
nowhere
somewhere
there

How
bravely
delightfully
happily
lazily
neatly
quickly
slowly

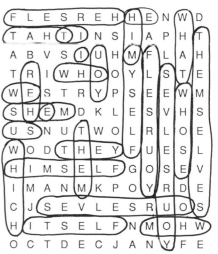

```
T E A R L Y G I F T E N
C Y N C S L O L P H E E
D I Y A O A L A M E R N
A N W A O C K Z D N E E
I C H T N I O I N E H A
Y A E R E T A L T T W T
L B R A V E L Y H F E L
W Y E R E H C O E O M Y
O L O N B N E H R E O R
L P N O W H E R E S S
S F U W C Q U I C K L Y
Y L I P P A H K V I L D
C A P R A L W A Y S S A
Y L L U F T H G I L E D
T E V E R Y W H E R E A
```

Page 54 — Pronoun Search

NOTE: Answers within each category may be in any order. Also, the shorter pronouns appear in many locations in the puzzle.

Personal
he · she
her · them
him · they
I · us
it · we
me · you

Reflexive
herself
himself
itself
myself
ourselves
themselves
yourself
yourselves

Relative or Interrogative
that
what
which
who
whom
whose

```
F L E S R E H H E N W D
T A H T I N S I A P H T
A B V S I U H M F L A H
T R I W H O O Y L S T E
W E S T R Y P S E W M
S H E M D K L E S V H S
U S N U T W O L R L O E
W O D T H E Y F U E S S
H I M S E L F G O S E V
I M A N M K P O Y R D E
C J S E V L E S R U O S
H I T S E L F N M O H W
O C T D E C J A N Y F E
```

Page 55 — Book Ends

1. cardboard   2. permitted   3. advertise
4. continent   5. dangerous   6. poisonous
7. necessary   8. departure   9. courteous
10. customary   11. pollution   12. advantage
13. telescope   14. candidate   15. construct
16. evaporate   17. operation   18. orchestra
19. therefore   20. sorrowful

Page 56   Job Hunting
1. lifeguard   2. astronaut   3. detective
4. carpenter   5. secretary   6. physician
7. ecologist   8. president   9. architect
10. professor   11. counselor   12. principal
13. conductor   14. biologist   15. scientist
16. librarian   17. announcer   18. publisher

Page 57   A Pair of Pears
1. arc, ark   2. callous, callus   3. peddle, pedal
4. you, ewe   5. soared, sword   6. reign, rain
7. meet, meat   8. lone, loan   9. hymn, him
10. peek, peak   11. seize, seas   12. pour, pore
13. daze, days   14. flee, flea   15. real, reel
16. beet, beat   17. haul, hall   18. air, heir
19. liar, lyre   20. maze, maize

Page 58   End to End
NOTE: Answers may vary.
1. twenty   2. route; south; mouth   3. alien; flier;
plied   4. steam; steal; stead   5. fuse; muse; just;
dust; must   6. course   7. aware   8. stage
9. spent; spend   10. proper; propel   11. swing;
owing; twine   12. planet; planed   13. caper; taper;
paper; gaped   14. earth; party   15. pearl; heard;
heart; teary; weary   16. scary; scare   17. frame
18. abuse   19. level; seven; fever; lever; never;
sever   20. wagon   21. moment   22. street
23. known; snowy   24. speak; spear

Page 59   Double End to End
1. distant   2. produce   3. highway   4. ceiling
5. oatmeal   6. bicycle   7. prairie   8. grocery
9. curtain   10. against   11. kitchen
12. mistake   13. surface   14. worship
15. promise   16. jealous   17. capture
18. explore   19. prevent   20. perhaps

Page 60   It All Adds Up
1. cotton   2. rather   3. history   4. target
5. legend   6. behave   7. carrot   8. meant
9. nomad   10. handbag   11. napkin
12. fortune   13. heart   14. winking
15. surface

Page 61   Double Up
Answers will vary. Possibilities include:
1. ribbon, hobble, rabbit
2. accept, soccer, raccoon
3. add, pudding, ladder
4. keep, green, street
5. traffic, muffin, difficult
6. juggle, bigger, shaggy
7. jackknife, bookkeeper
8. shell, million, jolly
9. hammer, mammal, scrimmage
10. tennis, kennel, innocent
11. spoon, broom, woodpecker
12. apple, zipper, suppose
13. hurry, arrow, parrot
14. pass, message, glasses
15. letter, kitten, cottage
16. buzz, grizzly, blizzard

Page 62   Evolution
Answers will vary; suggestions are given below.
1. home - some - sore - wore - work
2. foot - boot - bolt - bold - bald - ball
3. east - last - past - pest - west
4. love - dove - dote - date - hate
5. boat - coat - chat - chap - chip - ship
6. hand - band - bond - fond - food - foot
7. book - bark - bare - pare - page
8. seat - beat - best - bust - dust - dusk - desk
9. sock - soak - soap - slap - slip - slop - slob
10. rule - role - mole - male - mare - care